TALES OF THE UNEXPECTED

Edited by Dave Thomas

First published in Great Britain in 2000 by
YOUNG WRITERS
Remus House,
Coltsfoot Drive,
Woodston,
Peterborough, PE2 9JX
Telephone (01733) 890066

HB ISBN 0 75431 751 X
SB ISBN 0 75431 752 8

FOREWORD

This year, for the first time ever, Young Writers proudly presents a showcase of the best mini sagas from over 2,500 up-and-coming writers nationwide.

To write a mini saga - a story told in only fifty words - much imagination and skill is required. *Tales Of The Unexpected* achieves and excels these requirements and this exciting anthology will not disappoint the reader.

The thought, effect and hard work put into each mini saga impressed us all and the task of editing proved challenging due to the quality of entries received, but was nevertheless enjoyable. We hope you are as pleased as we are with the final selection and that you continue to enjoy *Tales Of The Unexpected* for many years to come.

CONTENTS

The Mini Sagas

WHO IS IT?

A devil with no horns, screeching, arguing and heavy stomping. Her heart as black as the night sky with eyes like flames of fire. Then to tease, she becomes quiet and gentle like a lamb, who is this person? Why my big sister!

Clare Rickard (9)

GIVING UP!

I practised day and night,
I tore my hair out,
I racked my brains.
What could I do?
How am I supposed to do it?
Ideas came and went,
Paper piled higher and higher.
Oh, I don't know,
I can't do it!
I'm giving up on this mini saga!

Amy Coombs (10)

MINI SAGA OF ERIC THE VIKING

Eric's deep blue eyes, angry. He had borne the hatred of his brother for years, now was his prime chance. He crept in. Beforehand he had decided on a slow, painful death. Eric opened his drinking flask and poured the dark, poisonous liquid into his twin's flask. He grinned, evilly.

Sajjad H Hassam (10)

ON THE BRIDGE

The wind whipped her hair against her cheeks. She sat precariously on the bridge rail. A slow tear ran down her bruised face into the dark water. 'Go on' screamed her mind. She knew it was for the best. There was nothing left to live for.

Calmly,
      Deliberately,
            She jumped.

Hannah Rickman (10)

TRAITORS GATE

I walked slowly through Traitors Gate, the traitor's screams torturing me. I walked up to the gallows as the traitor arrived and was placed upon it.

'Awful day isn't it?' he said.

'You shouldn't worry, I've got to walk home in it!' I replied as I kicked his stool away.

Matthew Wright (10)

FREEDOM

Did something move?
Was there a face at the window?
I really shouldn't have come.
There it was again! A movement inside the house,
something white.
There was a screaming sound - I realised it was me!
The thing suddenly came towards me
'Aaaaahhhhh!'

Poor little Snowy Owl, finally free.

Nicole Keightley (10)

A Bedtime Tale

The mist closed in around her, enveloping her in an endless stream of dense vapour. She could no longer see anything but a blur. All her senses were failing, even her mind was reaching termination, then blackness. It had happened, she had fallen asleep, book on her chest.

Ruth Prior (10)

TORTURE

The gloved, rubber hand of the insane escapee slipped over my mouth. I tried in vain to scream as he drew nearer, clutching the instruments of torture while his accomplice held me down. I could feel my life slowly slipping away . . .

'Calm down' cried the dentist, 'it's only a filling.'

Rosalind Thomson (11)

THE PENALTY

He sauntered to face his destiny,
if he didn't do it accurately and
professionally, England lose.
Was the pressure too hot to handle?
The tension. We'll have to wait and see.
Only seconds more. A silent prayer.
A step forward. Southgate shoots.
They think it's all over . . .
it is now.

Scott McGiveron (11)

A MURDER LURKING BEHIND A BLADE

There was evil within her, what else could it be? She was much too quiet to be innocent. I could prove her guilty and be the heroine of the town!

Then I stood up and saw her grasping a piercing blade!
'I don't think you'll get the chance . . . do you?'

Lucy Tucker (11)

CAPTIVE

High above the churning sea,
An ominous tenebrosity broods,
A moribund felon despairs,
He stares glumly out of the barred window,
Compunction overwhelms him.
In the esoteric, nefarious fortress dungeons,
There is no hope of escape
Out of the stygian gloom.
Then, a jingle of keys,
An open door,
Freedom!

Laura Wills (11)

LIFE OR DEATH

The campaign had begun, it was a matter of life or death. The coast was clear. I crawled through the furry undergrowth. The kitchen door was open, I dived through and checked for the enemy. There was my goal, tall and regal. I grabbed it, the cookie jar was mine.

Ben Blagden (12)

GANGLAND WARFARE

The coast was clear as I set off at a run. I dived. Squatting behind a wall as the enemy approached.

Perspiration trickling down my face. The gun in my clammy hand. I heard a low laugh behind me.
Swiftly turning. 'Ahh!' I screamed . . . as water soaked my swimming costume.

Ceri Pedrick (12)

THE ATTACK OF THE PURPLE HANDED MONSTER

We ran into the dark tunnel.
There came a long howl.
From the darkness came the monster.
Its claws were dripping.
We screamed and charged through the tall grass.
He was closing fast.
We ducked down and waited for the kill.
'I got some blackberries' said Alex.

Lisa Morris (12)

INTO THE UNKNOWN

I was full of anticipation that morning. I had spent the whole night there, and now I was so tense my entire body ached.

I sat, paralysed with fear, watching every move they made.

When they finally approached me I shook uncontrollably.
'Congratulations, it's a boy!' announced the doctor.

Kathryn Whiffen (12)

THE EXPERIENCE OF THE ECLIPSE

A sepia tone lingers outside. Birds are chorusing, soaring above. Darkness slowly but majestically overpowers light. The moon has been given a sovereign power, magnificently hiding the arc of fading sun. The splendid corona bursts into the unilluminated sky, sun rays twinkling round the edges. A truly unforgettable sight.

Caroline Mulholland (12)

IMPACT

They'd picked their targets. Just waiting for the moment of impact to show their strength, their power. Their intentions to provoke their prey. They prepared for attack. Not long to go now, their journey was nearly over. Closer, closer and . . . impact.

'Mum why didn't you bring the umbrella?'

Cara-Jade Johnson (12)

WAR!

Both sides charged. People flung themselves at each other, both sides determined to win. There was wailing echoing all around. People collapsed, injured.

I stood back, surveying, what was I to do to stop this terrible war?
'Stop everybody!'
But after all, what was a sleepover without a pillow fight?

Georgina Giles (12)

Clean Escape

All of a sudden we are pulled towards it. Blue, sharp teeth are whizzing and whirling around us. Foamy, frothing liquid from its jaws cascades around us, blinding us. It tries to suck us up, it pulls us towards it.

The end is near . . . We drive out of the car wash!

Kelly Wilson (12)

CAUGHT BY THE UNKNOWN

I slowly went deeper into the darkness. A shiver shot down my spine as something suddenly wrapped itself around my foot, I looked down. A green cord was waving around below me. My arms and legs kicked and waved frantically and I let out a deep breath.

I hate seaweed!

Gemma Lardner (12)

HALLOWE'EN NIGHT, TRICK OR TREAT

As she plunged the knife deeper into the object she laughed as she carved in shapes, deeper and deeper. She pulled it out for the last time, she sliced off the top and pulled out the insides. The finished product, 'Here you go,' said my mum handing me the pumpkin.

Leanne Jackson (12)

THE PIANO PLAYER

Sitting on her antique, wooden piano stool,
Dark red velvet covers the foam seat,
The beige and red patterned hemming neatens the edge.
Her back perfectly straight,
Her fingers swiftly gliding over the off-white keys,
Her dark blue eyes concentrating on the black notes printed in front of
her.

Agatha Baczkiewicz (12)

VIRTUAL CALAMITY

He placed himself in the leather seat, fastened his seatbelt and took off. Something was wrong. He was hurtling towards the cliff edge. With his brakes immobilised, death seemed certain. The engine roared . . . *crash!* Was he over with? Only his ride had finished when he heard 'please insert coin'.

Lewis Iwu (12)

OFF WITH HER HEAD!

'Off with her head!' screamed the eight knights as they plundered towards the beautiful princess, her long, blonde hair blowing in the wind. She had no escape. The knights vigorously chopped her head off with their swords.

The bedroom door opened. 'Mum, Richard's pulled the head off my new Barbie!'

Rachel Kelly (12)

CHEST PAINS

Just one last check to make sure he was completely knocked out, then slowly I dug the knife in, just above his heart. His chest opened, I pulled out his heart; the blood ran all over my hands. I replaced it with another heart. Another successful heart operation!

Katie Stretton (12)

RELUCTANT

I'm only young, this can't happen to me. I ran to my room and locked the door. I hid in my wardrobe, scared. I'm not going out of this room. I won't do it, I can't do it. The door strained to open. I shouted, 'I'm not doing the washing-up!'

Alexandra Read (12)

BRISK WITH THE WIND

The wind pushing, gliding it along. It slowed. Suddenly, out of the gloom came a whoosh, with flourish and excitement it lurched forward. It ground to a halt. Directly in front was a huge, towering obstacle. It pondered, then launched itself at the mountain. It soared. It landed. Lifeless.

Robert Wiesner (12)

PE

They ran, not daring to look behind them. Their cold breath rose into the air and slowly dispersed. The two girls stopped, gasping for breath while the others carried on. The hills were steep and needed a lot of energy to climb up. They had to, it was cross-country.

Rhona Morris (12)

Mini Saga

I stepped in cautiously. I had been here before many times. I thought I knew what to do. I turned the dial to the left. The icy shock was painful. I quickly turned it to the right. I leapt from the steam. This shower is useless, I'm having a bath.

Edward Greenwood (12)

The Determined Train

Colourful, open-topped carriages bursting with people, the cheerful train struggled to reach the top, slowly chugging up the bright red track.

And the people - their hair blowing gently in the breeze, finally reached their destination.
'Look!' I pointed to the train, and the speeding roller-coaster plunged down.

Sarah Ghori (12)

THE HUNT

I watched carefully for the beast I was hunting,
I listened intently for its sound,
Then suddenly I saw it,
I couldn't let it see me.
My heart was pounding as I moved closer,
I held my breath as I neared my enemy,
Then . . .
Splat! And the fly was dead.

Nicola Potter (12)

THE DANGERS OF SURPRISING THE ENEMY

The enemy advanced, walking steadily forward. It knew it had precise weaponry and would not stop until I was defeated. I turned to run but it just kept coming. I stumbled, fell and got up again, but it was too late. The skunk turned and fired with deadly pinpoint accuracy.

Hazel Sumner (12)

STORMY DAYS

As quick as I ran,
To get away,
I was hit more and more.
My heart was thumping so hard,
My legs were like jelly,
I was cold and wet,
My fingers were numb,
But I kept on going.
I reached for the door,
'Do you sell umbrellas, please?'

Emma Foster (12)

ALIEN EXTRACTION?

All I remember was the disc of light above me, a sharpness of pain, and then nothing. Nothing until I came too . . . Surrounded by whiteness I heard strange voices, saw strange faces.

The coldness of steel clenching white enamel, a crunch of bloody softness, and my tooth was out.

Jennifer Stanley (12)

Would I, Or Would I Not?

The decision was painful,
The thought eroded my brain,
Mankind was pushing me from every edge possible,
It kept me vigilant when the stars were glittering,
And when the sun blazed down,
The question that bore into me,
Would I get my hair cut?

Robyn McAllister (12)

THE RAGING WAR

The battle started,
Fierce warriors hungry for blood.
The field was muddy and wet.
All at once they charged into battle.
Hundreds were wounded.
After, the victors cheered,
While the defeated lay dejected.
Suddenly came a cry from afar,
'Jimmy put away your toy soldiers and come to dinner.'

Rachael McCrisken (12)

My Bombshell Bedroom

Shuddering, I stared across the dense battlefield complete with bodies scattered alongside. Ashamed of what had happened, what I had done.

I felt a tear dampen my right cheek. I took hold of my weapons, the duster, brush and mop, braced for my dirty, disgusting enemy . . . *my bedroom!*

Catherine Moorhead (12)

MYSTERIOUS RAIN

It plummeted down as if it was lead. It felt as if it was piercing my skin so fast I could not cry out. It fell in mists of grey and blue until the sky began to clear. Then the rain was no more and a burning sun was revealed.

Sophie Miller (12)

DENIZEN OF THE DEEP

As I sank into the water
I felt strangely warm,
It was then that I saw the fin.
I recognised it at once - '*Shark!*'
It grabbed my leg and pulled downwards,
I couldn't move . . .
It was then I heard the cry from above,
'Have you finished in the bath yet?'

Elizabeth Southgate (12)

MUM'S SPECIALITY

The wind whistles through cracks in the old house, a shadowy figure bustles about, raw flesh in one hand, a spear with the other, she stirs broth in a cauldron, with a large, wooden spoon, the flesh bubbling, she spoons sloppy mixture onto platters, suddenly she yells, *'Kids, tea's ready!'*

Lisa Jane Cowap (12)

HIDE AND SEEK

He approached my hiding place. I slowly crouched lower trying not to rustle the leaves. He retreated. I let out a long, silent sigh. I felt a twitch in my nose, my worst fear had come, I sneezed! Hurried footsteps approached.

'Caught!' he cried, 'great hiding place, let's have dinner.'

Nicola Butler (12)

MINI SAGA

They came up behind me
like a pack of wolves
closing in for a kill,
determined to devour every last
drop of blood in my body.
The scent of fresh, sweet blood attracts
them towards their evening meal.
Of all people it had to be me!

The mosquitoes strike again!

Olivia Cairns (12)

SHE CREEPS

'Are you sure?' the voice asks.

'No trouble at all,' she replies.

She lets the phone drop from scarlet tipped fingers. The darkened corridor looms, as the creeps. She sneaks into the study, the man doesn't see her. Her arm slips around his neck.

'Daaaddy, can Anna come round, pleeeeaase?'

Eleanor Ball (12)

TOTAL ECLIPSE

I walked down a bright and beautiful meadow, full of heavenly scents and colour. As I was walking, I felt a feeling of anxiety. I felt as if someone was lurking behind me. Suddenly it went startling dark, I looked back and saw the most tremendous sight of the
Eclipse . . .

Emma Claire Hasson (12)

HIM

I pushed past the crowd and saw him.

He was completely naked. Open eyes stared out of a deathly white face. One arm was strangely bent, the stiff hand clutching something. The coldness of his skin sent shivers through me.

I will never forget him. Michelangelo's David.

Danielle Zandi (12)

THE COOKIE JAR

I cornered the prey,
It was stuck,
I effortlessly swiped it off the shelf.
It fell and fell,
Until at last it hit the floor and broke
It lay shattered, helplessly immobilised.
Another jar wasted but,
A full stomach on the cookies inside.

Shiva Radhakrishnan (12)

THE STRUGGLE

I pulled but he pulled harder.
I twisted and put all my force into this battle.
He tugged and I yelled furiously.
He was gaining strength and winning.
Adrenaline flowed through me and I pulled viciously.
His face went red.
I wouldn't let him win.
Yes I got the remote!

Arooj Azam (13)

THE BATTLE

He was two feet taller than me,
His muscles rippling,

But I had to fight him,
I had to win,
My life depended on it.

He was overpowering me,
I couldn't take the strain,
His strokes were just too powerful.

I lost,
'Game, set and match!'

Gareth Ingle (12)

THE BANQUET

I enter the banquet hall at the end of my long awaited 'Tudor' day at the manor. I study Henry VIII. His costume, his face, are so like his portrayals. Suddenly, he looks at me. Startled, I glance down at my brochure. I freeze. There is no banquet scheduled for tonight.

Jennifer Brown (12)

THE MONSTER AND I

There I stood scared of the monster,
its green eyes glaring, its yellow teeth
showing. There we stood anxiously
awaiting the individual who would
make the first few steps towards the
milky goodness. The monster gave in,
took the first few steps and . . . *clap!*
The mouse trap shut!

Pierre Codson-Amamoo (12)

MINI SAGA

We faced each other. He regarded me with pure animal passion. *I* was holding his prize. Soon he would be moving in for the kill. I had to move - and quickly. Dodging him, I raced to the end and threw. The whistle rang out shrilly - my team had won!

Rachel Wetherfield (12)

DON'T GET CAUGHT

It was a regular thing
Scary, but had to be done
It was expected and waited for.

I reached for it
Silently, slowly
My hand closed around it
I brought it
Nearer,
To my head.

My other hand now reached
For the awaited.
They made contact . . .
'*Beep.*'
'Don't you dare use that phone.'

Sarah Saywell (12)

HIDING OUT!

I'm hiding in a dark corner, all is silent, suddenly I hear footsteps coming towards me, I try to escape, but it's too late, I feel a strong hand on my shoulder, a deep voice yells:
'Gotcha!'
My heart sinks when I hear the same voice again . . .
'Tag, you're it!'

Amie Smith (12)

A Simmering Saga

The constant ticking was driving me insane. The adrenaline was pumping, my heart was throbbing.

Like fleas the droplets of water catapulted themselves out of the container.

A burst of sound brought me back down to earth. It was a ringing, ringing, exploding noise. Silence . . . my egg was ready.

Victoria Macdonald (12)

DETERMINATION

She looked into his eyes,
As he looked into hers,
They each took a step forward
Their heavy breathing
The only sound.
They each had one thing in mind
Winning the prize,
This was important
The thing that meant power.
This would draw the line . . .
The last beefburger.

Laura Munt (12)

ALL CREATURES GREAT AND SMALL

They came from afar; tall, thin, fat, small - all different shapes and sizes.

The colours were spectacular, some walked, others jumped, few flew. Each individual making their own noise, each thankful to the man who was saving them.

The time had come; Noah had led them all into his ark.

James Dyke (12)

DREADFUL EXPERIENCE

I'll never be able to face anyone again. The horror of it all. I could hear people laughing and pointing at me. Everyone stared in astonishment. I'll have to move town, change my name. I can't bear thinking about it. The humiliation . . .

'Siobhan get a grip, you only fell over.'

Siobhan Mangan (12)

WORLD WAR III, CHESS STYLE

They prepare their armies, ready to do battle. The soldiers go forth, followed by the cavalry, heavy losses ensued, attacks, counter-attacks. The enemy strikes boldly, his artillery move into position but the king escapes. Victory will come soon as the other army launches a massive attack and finally . . . *checkmate!*

Alexander Shires (12)

BACK TO SCHOOL BLUES

The enormous feeling of disappointment and grief surged through me, up through my throat and out my mouth. A huge wail escaped and I started crying.

'Oh, come on, darling,' Mum said, impatiently.

'It's just so horrible,' I sniffed.

'Tough luck. You're going back to school and that's that!'

Leila Panesar (12)

THE BLACKOUT

There is banging and crashing,
people screaming with fear.
Another bang followed by another
scream. Suddenly the lights go out,
so this is what a blackout is like.
Then the darkness is shattered by
a flash of white and yellow that
covers the sky . . .
'Mummy is the storm over yet?'

Rachel Rennie (12)

FLOOD

Ah! We'll be flooded, quick run! They had to run for cover or else they would all die. The water poured down and everything was washed away. Families were separated and the screaming was horrific! The mud beneath them was their sanctuary.

'Mum, I'm finished watering the plants!' said Jane.

Kathryn Muir (12)

VICTORIAN SPLENDOUR

She's dressed to perfection with her little straw hat. She graces the Victorian landscape with her long, golden curls and sparkling blue eyes. The small, pink rosebuds on her satin and lace dress, glisten in the summer sun. Her cream buttoned shoes determine her journey, my porcelain doll, Pollyanna.

Laura Price (12)

THE DAY THE DARKNESS CAME

Suddenly it went dark, it was weird, there was silence, the darkness gathered, a tangible force. I felt fear.
Click!
Fear wrenched my stomach once more.
Click!
I screamed 'Mum I need a new light bulb.'

Rachael Shayer (12)

A TAIL'S TALE

She could see it out of the corner of her eye, following her wherever she went. She pounced to catch it by surprise but it moved with her. Round in circles she went but couldn't catch it.

Silly thing, she didn't realise it was her own tail.

Lauren Coe (12)

THE DUEL

I approached my enemy again,
determined to win this time.
The fight began!
Pushing, pulling, twisting, shaking.
It enveloped me, trying to suffocate me.
I was losing the battle,
must get help!
Sweating and struggling, finding a burst of energy
I shouted . . .
'Mum, I cannot get this duvet cover on!'

Bethany Key (12)

WAR

With my army behind me, I walked onto the battlefield. We were strong but were we up to the challenge?

With a desire for honour, I had chosen five courageous warriors. Our battle plan agreed, and we were ready for combat.

We pulled and won the 'Tug of War'.

Brioni Bradbeer (12)

FANTASY OF THE NIGHT

The stallion rose onto his hind legs, fire glowing in his bright eyes. I climbed aboard his silky back and together as one we galloped into the ever darkening night, jumping everything in sight. Thud. I awoke staring at the elegant rocking-horse, fire captured in his eyes.

'Kara, breakfast's ready!'

Kara Millhouse (12)

A SPLIT SECOND, THAT'S ALL IT TOOK

We all stood perfectly still, frozen to the spot. None of us dare move.
He picked it up and pointed it directly at us, that was when it happened,
he pulled back the trigger, a sudden surge of light raced towards me.
'Oh, I hate having my photo taken!'

Ellen Thornber (12)

THE ECLIPSE: AS SEEN ON TV

'First contact' - I'm excited, yet somehow worried.

While the fiery sun is being devoured by the moon, day slips into night.
My heart beats faster and louder, pumping, pounding.

Just two breathtaking minutes, then it's all over. Totality has come
and gone. The Eclipse is moving on.

Kathryn Garnham (12)

THE POWER

The darkness wrapped around me like a black cloak,
Everything was still,
silent.
I could hear the rustling of leaves outside.
I felt cold,
like someone had turned off the heating in winter.
I started to get scared.
Suddenly there was light.
'Just a power cut,' said my dad.

Beth Ainslie (12)

WATER WIMP!

The water mauled me. I was sure that the next wave would envelop me, like a monster's jaws.

I felt hopeless against the surging tide, my stomach churned. I simply could not compete with such strength . . .

So I swore, there and then, I would never go paddling again!

Lauren Harness (11)

THE DREADED DUNGEON

I lay waiting for tomorrow. There are many definitions of this dreaded place. It is a dungeon filled with powerful demons, which we are forced to attend. They are rewarded with treasures for persecuting us. When we are finally released, they leave us something far worse than hell itself . . . homework!

Francesca D'Souza (12)

IT'S YOUR TURN

'It's your turn,' they say. It always seems to be my turn, why is it never *their* turn?

I tell them I won't do it, one of them has to.

The thing is I don't see why *anyone* should have to do it, why can't we just get a dishwasher?

Jenny Lyons (12)

A CLOSE ENCOUNTER

It came thunderously before my eyes.
I struggled to move.
My heart was pounding.
I regretted taking part.
It got closer.
I promised myself I would be successful.
It was dreadful.
I took my chances.
I swung my arm with all the force I could manage.
I hit a six.

Tahir Iqbal (12)

WARFARE

I loaded my gun.
I cocked it.
Beads of perspiration dripped down my neck.
I was ready to fire.
It was heavy in my hands,
My stomach was in knots.
I fired.
'Take that!' I yelled at my friends,
As I squirted them with my water pistol.

Michael Frankland (12)

PAIN

I flew down thinking I would fall into oblivion but, then a thud, the pain of the blow seared through me, hands came to grab me, I cried out in agony.

I awaited apprehensively, for the final spasm of pain . . .
'TCP should heal it nice and quick now love.'

Zoë Puttock (12)

THE DEADLY GAME

I was surrounded. I knew I had to pass or else he would destroy me. He had blocked me from every direction. I had nowhere to go. I was about to surrender until I saw a blank space. I moved my queen to the empty pitch.

'Checkmate,' I said.

Shammi Rahman (12)

THE PREDATOR AND HIS PREY

The predator stalking his prey,
A silent, watchful game,
A game with deadly intent,
The prey goes blithely about its business,
The predator times its attack,
Crouches low,
In the long, yellow grass,
A twitch of the ear,
A flick of the tail,
Whoosh!
The tom-cat pounced,
And is rewarded.

Catherine Houlder (12)

MY DINNER IS YOU!

I travelled all day without food
In the bitter weather
I am lying on a branch
Getting ready to pounce,
I am very fierce
And I'm very dangerous
Get ready!
Because when you walk past
I am going to leap
So get ready for death
Because you are my . . .

                              Dinner!

Adam Hughes (13)

THE ECLIPSE

The moon and the sun were getting closer together, like gravity was pulling them.

In the grim sky I saw the sun, it was like a creature had taken a bite out of the large, yellow ball.

It was like millions of voices crying out in anxiety . . . *then silence.*

Pierce Cannon (12)

I WAITED

I waited, I focused, I heard the gun,
And I ran as fast as I could.
    I could feel myself getting hot,
but I knew I'd do it.
    I could see the end,
faster I ran, *whoosh* I ran into the rope.
    I'd made it, now I've got the
                    relay!

Ceri Joslin (12)

TOTAL ECLIPSE?

It was five minutes past eleven. The sky slowly turned dark until it was as black as night. The birds stopped singing, then suddenly the temperature dropped dramatically. I felt a cold shiver go up my spine, I was motionless. Then the heavens opened.

'Oh no it's raining!' I yelled.

Gary Over (12)

THE VISIT!

Silver point jabbing around,
soft, fleshy, pink mass.

Thundering vibration,
shook my whole being,
as the masked shadow stood above me.

A cold, solid, metal monster,
sucking, searching, slurping.

Silver larva flowing freely.

Packing, padding, squeezing,
forcing down.

Pink vulgar liquid swirling in waves,
suddenly gone into a silver hole.

'It's all over, tooth filled.'

Marc Hall (12)

THUMP

I have been searching for days.
There is no end to this sea of heat.
Thump! Thump!
My mount chews away at nothing; monotonous, apathetic.
His footsteps leave imprints on the bright sands.
Thump! Thump!
As I walk I search the horizon for a trace of green.
I am hopeful.

Ruth Wake (12)

UNDER PRESSURE

The frayed rope suddenly became taut as
the judge lifted his hand to start the competition
final.

Five tense minutes passed . . .

I began to feel the first bead of sweat.
It trickled down my cheek like a neglected
icicle on Christmas Eve.

The opposition pulled strongly - the rope gave way.

Luke Dyer (12)

DEATH - OR MAYBE NOT!

Running through the forest,
Carefree no longer.

He had to get away
Get away from the monster . . .
Or die.

The monster came closer
Much nearer now -
He ducked his head,
Waited to die.

A shadow fell over him
The monster lifted its foot . . .
Then . . . 'Mom! Watch out for the beetle!'

Naomi Noonan (12)

THE FACE

Alone in the house at night
A full moon shining.
The hairs on the back of my neck prickled.
A face!
Staring through my window!
Bright burning eyes, like fire
Sharp white teeth with cruel points.
A knock!
The door opened . . .
A werewolf!
'Trick or Treat!'

Tim Allen (12)

THE EVENT

The thought of being out there went into me like a knife.
As I prepared myself for this event, a shiver went down my spine,
I moved my legs so they hung over the edge and then . . . I stood up,
I had done it, I had got out of bed!

Kerri French (12)

WATER BATTLE

The fishing boat suddenly collided with the monstrous ship straight ahead. It tilted and fell mercilessly at the side of its victorious tormentor, who had followed the innocent boat, waiting to pounce.

Mission accomplished, the defeated boat sank into the dark murky world beneath the suds in the bath tub.

Aileen Riley (13)

Monstrous Footsteps

The heavy footsteps were coming, getting closer and louder.
I had to hide so that it wouldn't find me.
With nowhere to go, I was trapped.
Suddenly the monstrous thing was looming over me.
The deep voice said 'Go and tidy your room!'
'Oh Dad, do I have to?'

Christine Cooper

MOVING ON

I went to bed with a
heavy heart and dread
did its utmost to keep
sleep away. How can
my friends leave me
like this?

Morning broke too soon
and, bravely I faced the
day alone.

Tentatively, I entered the
building - my new school,
new teachers and new found
friends.

Ellen Bateman (13)

Silently Dead Windchimes

I was lost and alone, insecure
whilst engulfing my surroundings
like fire to my tranquil brain.

Then it calmly came. The gleaming
blade plunged through my helpless
body.

It went silent, deadly silent!

Only the wind chimes rang in their
repetitive formation.

My eyes closed and the heavens
silently opened.

Stevie Pease (13)

WAITING

The noise was deafening, hustle and bustle everywhere.
Strangers nudging me, where were they going, would they return?
I was going to have to pay when I left this commotion.

The time was here.
I could see it coming, getting nearer and nearer.
Slowly, then stopping - *my bus was here!*

Victoria King (13)

MY WALK IN THE DARK

My heart began to beat faster. I'm breathing faster.
Slowly I move forward towards the room that was
straight ahead, filled with darkness.
The floor's creaking with every step I take.
I reach a door.
I place my shaking hand on the door
I push it, I wait, silence!

Surprise!

Zahrah Mamode (13)

THE FAKE FOREST

I stumbled into the dark forest.
Crack! A twig splintered beneath my foot.
It was getting dark and I began to shiver
at the sudden temperature drop.
The shadows danced around me
and a noise penetrated the darkness.
I spun round - only to hear
'Get out of that display!'

Caroline Lacey (13)

FIRST STEPS

The room goes quiet for a few seconds, then there's a crash and toys go flying. The family gasps, but falls silent again. Another crash happens and milk spills all over the light blue carpet. But no one minds. As baby Tom finishes his first steps. Everyone smiles happily.

Amanda Young (13)

RUMOUR

Passing notes around the class,
From Ella to Sam and back again.
The rumour flies round, now everyone knows!
Only Sam was meant to know.
Jay's found out, I fancy him!
No one cares, not really,
Not like I thought they would.

Samantha Cornwell.

CLOSING IN

I'm cornered, pressed against a wall
with five guns all pointed straight at me.
My eyes dart quickly from my persecutors'
faces to their weapons. Narrowed eyes
and twitching fingers fill my mind as
adrenaline and fear take over.

Finally they pull the triggers.

The game is over, I'm soaked!

Amy Ross Russell

DEAD MEAT!

He picked up the knife, wiped it
and walked towards her with a
menacing smile.

He lifted the knife, it glistened
in the light.
He looked at her once again,
then without warning he plunged
the knife into her chest, slicing
into her.

'Dad! Have you carved the turkey yet?'

Louise Shaw (13)

The Animal Of My Dreams!

Prowling around, always alert, his eyes shine bright.
His ears prick up at every sound.
Sniffing his way through the long grass.
Birds flutter, lucky to escape.

Running energetically towards me, mouth open, slobbering.
His teeth are sharp as he grabs his ball.
He bounces, playing.
This is . . . my dog!

Laura Lomas (13)

The Chase

David was running with all his might.
Sweat was dripping from his brow.
His legs were aching.
He was being followed - there was no help at hand.
The end was in sight.
Then someone started to run towards him.
He dodged him.
Yes, he'd scored the winning try.

Chris Murray (13)

SPOOKY SURPRISE

As I entered the house I heard a noise.
Deep breathing was all around me.
I shivered and trembled with fear
As I stood in the gloom.
Then I felt a hand touch my shoulder.
Suddenly the lights came on.
I spun round . . . 'Surprise,
Happy Birthday!'

Sarah Louise Wiffen (13)

THE . . . THING

'I'm holding it in my hands!
Encased by the glass of the wooden frame
is a black thing - a hideous primordial ooze,
an amorphous slimy blob and its eyes are red,
its mouth is open for biting people's flesh.

'Shut up, it's only my picture!'
I said to my brother.'

Nadine Chatergon (13)

NATURE'S MONSTER

We're tired!
We have to escape the raging
yet beautiful monster behind us.
We were being dragged back!
It'll swallow us up, bit by bit.
No remorse!
The white and grey monster was close
'Grab the branch!' I heard.
Now all I could see was the waterfall,
swallowing my boat.

Kirsty Forbes (13)

HOUNDED

I was exhausted from running.
I lay down on the grass
and could hear his heavy breathing
moving closer.
I lay in silence.
He stopped behind me and I could
feel his hot breath on the back of my neck.
But I wouldn't be defeated.
'No! Bad dog!' I shouted.

Louise Neal (13)

UTTER HUMILIATION

The room falls silent
I glance at what I've got
It's not looking good!
The consequences are just too great.
I've come to a conclusion
I hold my breath and assemble
the answer . . .
The room fills with laughter
as my sister shrieks -
'Know how to spell before
playing Scrabble again!'

Danielle Leggatt (13)

HIS SECRET

What if Louise had already found her?
Ben had to get to Samantha quickly.
She couldn't yet know that he was
about to dump her!
He found Louise telling Samantha.
Ben watched her . . .
It was like a piece of delicate glass
being shattered into a thousand pieces.

Emma Scott (13)

BOMB SITE

I heard a roar from the General
and scrambled the last few feet
towards my destination.

As I saw the debris strewn around
I knew this was going to be a
difficult task and it would take me
days to complete.

I took a deep breath and entered
my bedroom!

Emma Sears (13)

HOSTAGE!

Abandoned, waterless, no sign of life.
Sunlight dazzles me and heat from the
sun pounds down on my back.

Some coarse cloth serves as a blindfold.
I'm tied and bound.
I hear my captors talking.
My life must surely end.

I am roughly thrown onto horseback.
Relief! A familiar voice.

Laureen Dimelow (13)

MISSION IMPOSSIBLE

We drag the growling monster towards the hostile building.
It bites at any flesh it sees - which for us is too much.
Blood oozes toward the surface of our skin.
A few metres and we will be there.
We arrive at last,
For our dog's annual check-up!

Craig Dooley

CLOSE ENCOUNTERS OF THE FURRED KIND

The creature stared, its deep expressionless eyes
glowing red.
I stared back, surprised!
A low growl sounded from the depths of its dark
furry chest.
It blinked once and pounced.
I felt a sharp pain as its fangs sank
into my flesh.
I screamed out -
'Mum, the hamster's escaped again!'

Joanne Naylor (13)

UNDER THE COVER OF DARKNESS

The bright light of the moon lit my path.
My way was clear, not a sound could be heard.
Under the cover of darkness I crept towards
the big white machine.
I opened up its doors.
The bright light shone upon my face.
It was time for my midnight snack.

Michael Leyden (13)

BMW (BATH MEANS WAR)

So the war rages on
between plastic duck city
and toy boat town.

Bombs are flying everywhere.
Look out! Oh no!
Two boats have sunk
The ducks have surely won the war.

Boom! Boom! Boom!
It's a nuclear explosion.

No. Just my mum
'Have you finished in the bath yet?'

David Evans (13)

ALIENS?

The illuminous disc flew up into space;
elegant and soundless.
It curved in an arc before crashing down
onto the planet it had just left.
One of the bystanders rushed towards
the fallen article, but it was too late -
'Katie! You missed the Frisbee again!'

Katie Potter (13)

FEAR OF THE NIGHT

The autumn leaves crunched under my feet,
As I ran far, far into the darkness.
The canvas house left behind.
My friend asleep, not knowing.
Not knowing of the stranger,
Following me into the night.
I heard a twig snap behind me.
Slowly, I turned around . . .
'Gotcha!' laughed my brother!

Laura Helen Marsh *(13)*

DARKNESS

Very late one night I was lying in my bed, terrified.
I could hear the slow breathing of something
lurking in my room.

'Who's there?' I asked - only a snarl replied.

Then it leapt on me - I saw its razor-sharp teeth.

'Fido,' I shouted 'go to your kennel!'

Emma Marshall (13)

THE GAME

She ran through the trees
gasping for breath.
She could hear footsteps coming closer.
'No he can't find me' she thought.
Her heart raced inside her
as he came nearer.
She dived behind a tree.
Had he seen her?
No!
Suddenly an arm grabbed her
'Tag! You're it!' he said.

Kayleigh Turner (13)

THE KILLING

I considered it to be manslaughter - not murder as such.
He had asked for it, although it had been too easy really.
He had been hovering around me, irritating and pestering me,
goading me into attacking him with the huge piece of wood . . .
Wham!
I have always hated flies.

Holly Holden (13)

FEELINGS OF DREAD IN MY STOMACH

I'm waiting in line . . .
He's up to the third one,
Not long until it's my turn.

Don't reach me!
I don't want to die!

He's on the fifth one now.
I'm next.

Think fast, invent an injury!
He won't fall for it.

'Emma?'
'Present Sir.'

Oh no! PE again!

Emma Champion (13)

MONSOON

The floodgates open with a rumble
Gallons of steaming water
Gush into the vast canyon.
Noise like an express train
Fills my ears
Geysers appear around the waterfalls.
As a mighty ocean liner floats by,
As I put in the soap and rubber duck,
And climb into the bath.

Gemma Walton (14)

LIFE'S A GAMBLE

My life was full of misery, chance and debt.
Wandering from street to street.
I had nothing.
No money
No property
My every move was a gamble
Full of tax payments
I spent most of my time in prison
My only hope now was to
reach '*Go*' and collect £200.

Joanna Challen (14)

An Arachnid's Fatal Mistake

Stuck within a vast white space.
There is no escape.
These walls are just too smooth to climb.
A bright light from above dazzles me.
There's a piercing scream.
Water begins to swirl around my feet.
I lose my grip and I'm sucked into the darkness
of the plughole.

Laura Varley (14)

WILD DREAMS

She crashed through the undergrowth,
the gnarled, tangled knots of roots
catching at her feet.

Her heart pounded against her ribcage
like a ferocious, urgent war cry and
her brain was sending frantic messages
of near paralytic fear.

It was gaining,
Then all went black.

She woke up!

Lizzie Birkett (14)

HE SHOOTS, HE SCORES

His path was blocked.
Two stood between him and victory.
He passed the first with skills no one could match.
His mind was focused, he would not be intimated.
He saw his chance and took it with pinpoint accuracy.
'Goal!' Cheered the ecstatic fans.

Amanda Hampson (14)

THE JOURNEY HOME

We staggered through the wild and endless forest
with our bags that weighed us down.
Our legs aching with the thought that there
would be more to come.
Nothing was to be seen,
We looked so hard, we tried so much!
Then we saw it,
Our *Home Sweet Home!*

Martine Landeman (14)

THE DANCING MAN

Like an arrow through air, he glided swiftly
on the shiny pearl ice.
As a sorrowful torture glared in his eyes,
when the magical dance changed into a
sacred ritual.
His mind, sculptured by hate was slowly dying.
Drifting away like a boat into sea,
He was the dancing man.

Abigail Gaughran (14)

DOES MURDER DAWN?

Silence, nobody said a word.
The door creaked open and darkness
was upon them.
There was a musty smell in the air
and you could see the fear in their eyes.
Then a single candlelit the room.
A voice groaned 'Welcome, I hope you enjoy
your Murder Mystery Weekend.'

Donna Marsh (14)

MAIL BREAKFAST

The beast waited in her den for the attack to begin.
Her jaws wide, mouth drooling.
Nose twitching
She'd smelt the blue overalls.
The attack began,
Position one, the lookout post.
Position two, through the fence.
Jaws straight into a nice rump steak.
'Mum! The dog's bitten the postman!'

Lyndsey Slaven (15)

ESCAPE

Heart pounding, blood racing,
she dodged behind the bins, out of sight.
There was little time before they all came out.
She scrambled up a tree and dropped down
over the barbed wire.
Free at last!
But a firm hand clamped down on her shoulder.
She turned slowly.
The Headmaster!

Joanne Osborne (14)

DANGER IN DOWNTOWN NEW YORK

Wandering, gun in hand, along the cold dark streets,
I scan the shadows.
A gunshot echoes far off in an alley,
and the sirens wail as the police speed past.
I dive into the nearest doorway, but I am not alone.
Pow!
Suddenly everything goes blank . . .
'Mum! The computer crashed again!'

Katy Barnard (14)

INGENIOUS TACTICS

His eyes glowing
His heart beating hurriedly
Watching my every move
As I stood up,
He hurled himself at my feet.
Bang!
I was down
I had to give in
He knew he had won!
As I placed the dog food in his bowl.
'You're a pest!' I sighed.

Angela Hammond (14)

SUMMER FREEDOM

Silence. Expectancy.
They hid, waiting for it to happen.
Then they heard it
At first it was just a distant rumble;
Like thunder.
Then the floor began to tremble.
The deafening roar grew louder.
Then faded.
Silence;
The mice had the school to themselves
for six weeks.

Hannah Morris (14)

THE ALMIGHTY STRUGGLE

The race was on, a life in great danger.
As the water twisted and turned in a powerful whirlpool,
you could see the last breaths being taken.
It was an almighty struggle for the creature.
The current dragged the lifeless spider down the plughole.
Never to be seen again.

Clare Ovenden (14)

UNTIL DEATH DO US PART

'I love you' he said again.
Somehow it seemed vital that she knew.
She tried to speak but couldn't.
Not because she was happy, but because of the pain.
this is not a love scene
this is the final exchange of words
between a husband and his dying wife.

Kara Critchell (14)

LET BATTLE COMMENCE

As soon as she said it, the battle began.
Without hesitation he made a break for the door.
In quick pursuit
she caught him round the waist and brought him
kicking and screaming to the room.
She pinned him down.
He was finally in bed,
There was just story time to go!

Laura Woodland (14)

SINKING

Gaping depths swallow me up.
Searching for a sign
I am met with endless darkness.
Terror and confusion.
Yet still I sink deeper.
I try to scream, but sound can't touch this world.
Suddenly, warmth and safety.
I close my tired eyes
And sink into welcoming, infinite sleep.
Then . . . Silence . . .

Iona Stephens (14)

WILD

Scavengers, hunters, hunted.
All are gathered here.
Some scream their strange blood-curdling calls
while others sit contented with shapes and colours.
A display of animals torn from their families,
each struggling to adapt.
I had to get out
Out of the place they call
'Happy Days Babycare.'

Eleanor Odom (14)

COLD CALLER

Moving quickly on
Sickening feeling
Fumbles for keys
Bolts the door
Light and safe now
Curtains drawn
Glances towards telephone
Prays that endless calls will stop
Kettle on
Strange noise outside
Doorbell rings
Dare she answer?
Man on doorstep . . .
'Good evening, Madam,
Have you ever considered
Double Glazing?'

Sonia Curley (14)

FLOOD DISASTER

Deeper and deeper the waters rose . . . with a roaring,
rushing sound, topped by an ominous foam.
Frothing.
First - ankle deep,
Then - higher and higher.

Was this the end?

Would the waves rise forever, covering the whole world?

Or was it time to pull out the plug and dry myself!

David Piper (14)

SLOWLY THE MIST

Sweat poured down Peter's face in torrents.
There was a roar like thunder and the dim glow
of the candle flickered then died.
It was dark and cold.
A thick mist was swirling around the bench.
The mist slowly cleared as the *beast* pulled into the station
Evacuees fleeing war.

Nicola Rider (14)

MELTING MOMENTS

Its surrounds began to cave in before melting into a soft slush.
The thick golden lava slowly emerged from its soft coating
then trickled out into the world before being washed away
and lost forever.

He peeled back the wrappers to reveal all.
Then popped another delicious *Rolo* into his mouth.

Kelly Fry (14)

As The Rain Dripped Down The Window

You lay there in the bed
Telling yourself to be brave
As everyone is born to die.
The grip you had on my hand loosened.
Your eyes began to close.
A tear fell from my eye
As the rain dripped down the window.
Your story had come to an end.

Hannah Steer (14)

BE BRAVE

'Come on Peter, you must go to school today.
I've got your favourite breakfast ready.'
'I don't want to go Mum!'
'Why not?'
'Nobody likes me. All the children make fun of me,
and the teachers don't like me either.'
'Don't be silly darling! You must go -
You're the *Headmaster!'*

Jonathan Davis (14)

A Hero's Death

'Mayday! Mayday!
I need immediate assistance.
I'm going down, my oxygen supplies are low.
My wings can't withstand the air resistance any longer.
The enemy is gaining on me.
I can't shake it off.
I can't shake it off.
Help! Mom it's alright - I got the fly!'

Sukhveer Bhaker (14)

Every Second Counts

The gunshot still ringing in her ears, she forced herself to run faster.
Her feet thudded painfully on the baked ground, but she knew,
for her daughter's sake she must continue.

Then behind her she heard laboured breathing, thudding feet,
a woman passed her.

Another Mother's race, another second place!

Natalie Baker (14)

DRAGON FROM HELL?

Like a dragon from hell, the beast lolloped down the hallway
developing a sudden craze of bloodlust.
As fast as I could, I ran!

Using my judgement of whereabouts,
I hid behind an obstacle.
As I prayed for survival,
The beast's jaws opened -
'Tidy your room!'
'Yes Mum!'

John Mackenzie (14)

MISSION IMPOSSIBLE

I had my mission drafted out in my mind.
I had to creep cautiously through the enemy territory.
It was as hazardous as passing through a minefield.
One false move and I would have been dead.
As I reached the forbidden container,
My mum shouted,
'No cookies until after dinner!'

Lauren Brown (14)

The Bathroom

There he sat in the corner;
My eyes caught on him like a thorn;
His darkness screamed in my ears;
His legs were wrapped around my chest;
Crushing me;
If I was to strike, it must be now;
So I grabbed a bar of soap and squashed the spider.

Julie Hannah (14)

METAMORPHOSIS

The sky darkened and draped a
colourless cloak over everything in sight.
Birds circled overhead.
Dainty flowers cowered against the icy wind.
The now frozen world seemed eerily still and dead.
Nothing breathed.
In the distance an agitated growl
broke into a thunderous roar.
The storm had begun.

Emma Jane Pegg (14)

Rising From The Darkness

All I could see was darkness
but as I pushed up I saw beads
of light in front of me. I felt
the fresh air caressing my
newly found body, as it cam
up out of the blackness. I
first felt the raindrops as they
crashed onto my leaves.

Kerry Adams (14)

SURRENDER

There was a moment of decision.
I could feel the tension building up between us.
There was no sense of retreat coming from it -
the persistence was burrowing into me, harder, harder.
I had no choice but to give in.
'I'll start my diet tomorrow,' I told my cream cake.

Katie Bowdrey (14)

CLOSED DOORS

She went further and further on, her arms beginning to ache
at the heavy weight upon her shoulders, her weary legs
feeling heavier at each step. On to the next house, then the
next. No one acknowledging her. Only another fifty more.
She should finish this paper round by six o'clock.

Louisa Burkin (14)

THE END DRAWS NIGH

The monster roared closer.
Andy's life was nearly over. He was
different from his friends; he
didn't fear death and prepared
himself for it.
'Jo, turn off the vacuum.'
Jo switched off the vacuum. The
monster was stationary. The bug
in the rug had survived yet another day.

Matthew Gardiner (14)

HER

The chatter dies,
the doors swing open
to reveal Her.
She confidently strides in
as the others look on in fear.
Before she even reaches the machine
they pick up the phone, ready.
She's now there - silence overwhelms everything.

'Sir, the computers have crashed.'
The cursed worker has struck again.

Sally Bouttell (14)

ANNIHILATION

There he was - directly in front
of me.
A little green man!
Suddenly, I felt an urge to
annihilate him.
Would I take the feet from under
him,
Or just go straight for his head?
I swallowed him whole instead.
Delicious Jelly Baby!

Joanne McCormack (14)

THE OGRE - MY BABY SISTER

This baby was not ordinary . . . its eyes were blood-red,
its fork-like tongue was lurking, menacingly behind
protruding, sharp, yellow teeth. Its long, spiky
fingernails were clawing my face. I reached,
desperately for my mother but she was simply
smiling adoringly at this ogre, repeating 'Smile for
Mummy, good girl!'

Joanne Mulholland (14)

THE MONSTER OF SUNDAY NIGHT

It's 11pm . . .
I sit, sweating, frantic and it is there.
I lay the beast before me, malicious
instigator of a thousand sleepless nights.
I pick up my pen but am unable to mark
its blank, yet grinning face.
Ghastly voices softly seem to whisper,
'I'm due in tomorrow.'

Becci Rose (15)

A Beginning, Middle And End

The beginning:
>   Swerving, sensing, searching.
>   The race is long and hard.
Existence.

The middle:
>   Laughing, living, loving.
>   The world at my feet.
Life.

The end:
>   Fighting, fearing, forgetting.
>   Gently it takes me.
Death.

Louisa FitzGerald (15)

WRITER'S BLOCK

Ideas have dried up,
He's tired and fed up.
An arid landscape of inspiration.

'*Wait!*' He thinks he's caught something -
'*Damn!*' It swam away before he could reel it in.
He knows there's something lurking
beneath the murky mists of his imagination.
Suddenly it bites.
He's written a saga!

James Tuffin (15)

ESCAPE

Geoffrey dug furiously while his companions kept watch.
Every breath of wind or rustle of leaves startled them.
They soon squeezed under the fence and made a mad
dash across the lawn but the warden soon captured
Geoffrey and shouted for back-up,
'Mum, the guinea pigs have got out again!'

Heather Edmonds (15)

THE VICTIM

The ominous shadow loomed towards her,
its warm breath nearing.
Pearly dewdrops fell onto her blotched face.
The plunge came as a red-hot knife,
Piercing deep into her soul.
The sweat-soaked flesh
And the crying of her soul ceased,
as the doctor withdrew the needle.

Caroline George (15)

Birthday Thief

The door was lying open, sure proof that
someone had broken in.
Very silently she crept into her house,
careful not to alert the burglar to her presence.
As she stepped into the hall she heard voices
in the TV room.
She threw open the door and froze . . .
'Happy Birthday!'

Natalie McGivern (15)

THE RACE

He ran and ran,
Looking behind him,
he could see his
opposition. The
next stage to this
race was up, up and
away. Up, up and
stop, the end of the
race. He won, he is
up the tree and safe
from the dog. The
squirrel will survive
another day.

Amanda Harper (15)

THE GAME

It was not a game, not anymore. It was
his life. He had used thoughtful planning
and money was not a problem. He lifted the
cube that would destine his future, and
looked on in suspense as it rolled. It stopped,
a sigh of relief. Mayfair was his!

Olivia Thornton (15)

TORTURE?

The heat is unbearable, my mouth has gone dry.
Sweat prickles on my top lip.
My head is heavy and my limbs are burning.
I try shifting my body, forcing it to move.
My strength is weakening and my mind is hazy . . .
No more sunbathing today for me!

Rebecca Carter (15)

POUNCE

He sneaked through the bushes gracefully,
without making a sound.
His eyes focused on the helpless victim.
He brought out his hidden weapons.
In one sleek movement, he pounced.
His victim gave a short struggle
before it was all over.
Then he moved, towards me . . .
dropped a mouse and purred.

Alex Carini (15)

GUILTY

Crouched behind the heavy oak door, I strained my ears.
If anyone found me I would be the clear culprit.
I heard footsteps within the room . . . and then silence.
The anticipation was indescribable, but sure enough it came,
The bellowing shout of my father.
He had discovered the broken vase.

Victoria Towler (15)

THE VIGIL

The moment was intense, we had to see him,
we had been up all night, my brother and I.
Sitting on the cold fireplace, next to the sherry,
mince pies and carrots for his reindeer, both
determined to stay awake. But when we awoke
next morning, he had already been.

Hayley Fitton (15)

SUMMER MEMORY

'Close your eyes' he said.
His smile glistened,
he lead me to the rounded pier
Where he came up behind me
And whispered 'Open your eyes.'
And there in front of me was a
beautifully glossed ocean.
I inhaled deeply as he touched
my face gently
and softly whispered 'Stay!'

Sian Hardie (15)

BATTLE DRONE

I watched my enemy. My knuckles
turned white as I gripped my weapon.
Beads of perspiration trickled down my
forehead. I breathed heavily in anticipation.
I was ready to attack.
My target darted swiftly towards me,
its monotonous drone filling the air.
I raised my arm . . .
'Got you, pesky wasp!'

Andrea Nirsimloo (15)

IMPENDING DOOM

Lined up, each awaiting our fate, the gun was poised;
an unnecessary reminder that the end beckoned.
He signalled to prepare ourselves.
Gazing intently towards the floor,
unanimously hoping ours would be the
quickest, easiest ending.
The gun rose, '*bang!*' My end was nearing.
The 100 metres final had begun!

Abigail Moore (16)

IN DARKNESS WE STRIKE

Each step I took
my heartbeat quickened.
My fellow beasts joined me.
I cracked an evil smile,
My last victim was
behind this door.
As darkness swirled
around us,
my fellow companions
nodded. I knocked . . .
We waited . . .
My victim opened the
door. We screamed
in unison,
'Trick or Treat.'

Amina Nakhuda (16)

FLYING DISASTER

Flying through the air, he prayed
that he wouldn't collide with them.

    Boom!

He hit the slightly globed surface
and the black arm compressed
his entire body to the transparent
mass beneath him.

I suppose that's what happens when
a bluebottle flies the wrong way up the M4!

Clare Sanders (16)

FLOWERS SLEEP

Nature called my name. As I ran
into the fields I realised the beauty
around me. The sun caressed my
every move and the flowers wept
in pure delight.
As my euphoria slipped through my
hands I ran faster, night followed
and the astral reeds called my name,
I began to fly.

Lucinda Wilkinson (16)

FEAR

It sucks out all rational thoughts, leaving me with only
an overactive imagination that feeds my paranoia,
like sharks feeding on their prey. It numbs my voice
so that all I can do is scream. Petrified, wanting help,
but I must kill it alone by facing it. Face your fear.

Emma Hordle (15)

PARTINGS

She clung on tightly as if she'd never let go,
the light reflecting powerfully off the cruel blades.
Closing her eyes, she hardly dared to breathe
as the icy chill approached her jaw.
Opening her eyes fearfully, she looked into the mirror.
Her hair lay motionless on the floor.

Judith Colvin (15)

MY FIRST BATH

Her firm hands enclosed me, distant from the safety
of her embrace. Unsure, I fruitlessly writhed, crying
for my freedom. Suddenly, she forced me down,
plunging me into a multitude of foreign tears.
I shrieked out the breath that dared to enter my lungs,
until her loving embrace quietened me.

Julie Woodfield (15)

FRIGHTENING JOURNEY

I looked at him, so serious,
his eyes fixed straight ahead.
If only I hadn't got in this car.
My stomach churning,
I clenched the seat,
Travelling down a deserted lane
until the car stopped.
He turned towards me and smiled.
'Well Mum, how was my first driving lesson?'

Jemma Feesey-Passmore (15)

IMPRISONMENT

I sit there in silence - I have committed an offence.
Then I stand, leaning against the wall with the
witnesses stating their side of the story.
The jury have to decide whether I am guilty of my crime.
The judge gives a verdict - guilty.
Sentence: After school detention.

Michelle De-Pass (15)

A LIVE AUDIENCE

The stage was set for embattlement, a small plain area.
Close by stood 10 or more people, slavering,
like rabid dogs to be set free to do battle.
Then a man with a microphone enters,
the crowd starts to cheer. Quietly and calmly he begins,
'Welcome to the Jerry Springer Show.'

Donna Chatfield (15)

AFTER MIDNIGHT

She shut the door behind her as quietly as possible.
She then turned towards the staircase and there he was,
anger in his eyes and the temper slowly rising.
She panicked, her heart thumping as if it were about to pop out.
'What time doe you call this Anita?' Said her father.

Minhazbanu Pathan (15)

ONE WORD ONLY

I imposed on a surface of debris,
Wooden floorboards creaked,
Voices probed my head,
My body froze instantly,
I swallowed and prepared for attack,
I grasped my hands firmly, tightly together - side by side,
I took a deep breath and I shouted out loudly,
'Shut up!'
Then everybody's teaspoons stopped moving.

Marie Elenà Buchanan (15)